DOG
BRAIN-TEASERS

Published by arrangement with
the British Broadcasting Corporation

Wherever appropriate all references and spellings
are taken from the Target novelisations

DOCTOR WHO
BRAIN-TEASERS AND
MIND-BENDERS

Adrian Heath

A TARGET BOOK

published by
the Paperback Division of
W. H. ALLEN & Co. Plc

A Target Book
Published in 1984
By the Paperback Division of
W. H. Allen & Co. Plc
44 Hill Street, London W1X 8LB

Printed and bound in Great Britain by
Anchor Brendon Ltd, Tiptree, Essex

ISBN 0 426 198603

CONTENTS

The Puzzles

The Answers

The Puzzles

1 So You Think You Know About Who?

1   In which story did the Doctor first use the sonic-screwdriver?
2   What type of TARDIS is the Doctor's?
3   What species uses a Mark Three Travel Machine?
4   What was K1?
5   What is Shada?
6   What was *Doctor Who and the Seven Keys to Doomsday*?
7   In what constellation is Gallifrey to be found?
8   When at the Academy on Gallifrey, all Time Lords are given an identification code. What was the Doctor's code?
9   What is Gallifrey's binary location from galactic zero centre?
10 In what story did the Cybermen make their debut?
11 In what galaxy is the planet Vortis?
12 By what name is the planet Xxbrmm now known?
13 By what name were the three Urbankans met by the fifth Doctor known?
14 In what constellation is the planet Castrovalva to be found?
15 What are the colours of the Patrex, Arcalian and Prydonian chapters of Gallifrey?
16 How was Davros crippled?
17 In a Sontaran ship what does CVT stand for?
18 Who was Kamelion impersonating when the Doctor first met him?
19 What was ECCO?
20 What grade did Romana get at the Academy on Gallifrey?
21 Ian was made a knight of which city?
22 In what mineral is the planet Exxilon abundant?
23 How many Osirians did it take to defeat and imprison Sutekh?
24 What does the Traken word 'Melkur' mean?
25 What was at the heart of the experimental grid on Argolis?

26 What is the natural form of a Zolfa-Thuran?

27 What University did Professor Marius go to?

28 Maxwell's Second Law of Thermodynamics contains two grim words. What are they?

29 From where does the ritual gesture of the Sevateem originate?

30 Where was the Doctor going for a holiday when he was summoned by the White Guardian?

31 Which magazine did Sarah Jane Smith write most of her material for?

32 What is the name of Atrios' sister planet?

33 Liz Shaw was a scientist at which English University?

34 When exactly was the first episode of *Doctor Who* first broadcast?

35 Who was the producer of *Doctor Who* for the whole of the Peter Davison era?

Once you have answered as many of these questions as you can, mark your answers from the list at the back of this book. Find out how good your *Doctor Who* knowledge rating is by consulting the following list:

0–15 You obviously don't know that much about *Doctor Who* yet.

16–25 Your knowledge of *Doctor Who* is quite good.

26–30 Your knowledge of *Doctor Who* is very good.

31–35 Your knowledge of *Doctor Who* is excellent.

2 Robots, Robots, Everywhere

If you track from letter to adjacent letter vertically (up or down) or horizontally (right or left) – no diagonals – on the grid, starting from the letter in the box, you can track out the names of ten robots or robotic species.

B	O	B	O	T	S	O	E	A	T
S	R	G	S	V	A	F	D	P	H
N	N	U	K	A	E	S	A	O	L
A	D	A	R	T	S	S	H	P	Y
A	D	U	O	R	A	N	T	B	O
T	I	Q	N	G	I	N	R	O	T
E	M	U	H	C	S	N	R	E	S
Y	B	L	N	O	I	A	V	O	R
S	E	I	A	S	D	L	L	T	O
M	E	C	H	M	O	V	E	O	B

3 Introducing Peter Davison

Re-arrange this mixed-up list of all the fifth Doctor's
adventures so that they are in the order in which they
occurred:

Enlightenment	*Terminus*
Kinda	*Time-Flight*
Castrovalva	*The Awakening*
Frontios	*Arc of Infinity*
Black Orchid	*Earthshock*
Warriors of the Deep	*Planet of Fire*
Snakedance	*The King's Demons*
The Five Doctors	*Resurrection of the Daleks*
The Visitation	*Mawdryn Undead*
The Caves of Androzani	*Four to Doomsday*

4 Which Planet?

1 Which planet in the Acteon Galaxy has been visited by the third Doctor?
   P Peladon
   Q Exxilon
   R Spiridon
   S Metebelis Three
   T Solos
2 Which of these planets has been visited by the fifth Doctor?
   A Deva Loka
   B Zolfa-Thura
   C Zeta Minor
   D Inter Minor
   E Sense-Sphere
3 Which of these planets was not visited by the second Doctor?
   F Skaro
   G Dulkis
   H Vortis
   I Ta
   J Telos
4 Which of the following pairs of planets have been visited by the fourth Doctor?
   A Alzarius, Spiridon
   B Aridius, Kembel
   C Peladon, Pluto
   D Tigella, Argolis
   E Zanak, Solos
5 Which of the five planets was the last of the five to be visited by the first Doctor?
   A Tigus
   B Aridius
   C Xeros
   D Mechanus
   E Vortis

Once you have got what you believe to be the five correct answers, take the letter representing each answer (if you think the answer to number 5 is Vortis you would take the letter E) and re-arrange them to form the name of a planet. What is special about this planet?

5 The Nestenes

This puzzle is a word search with a difference. Each different number represents a letter of the alphabet (with the same number always representing the same letter). For example, the number 12 may turn out to be X so you would write X in every square containing the number 12. Ten letters are given to you but working out the other sixteen is up to you.

S 11	15	14	I 2	7	O 22	15	14	E 15	16	16	15	14
25	25	14	7	15	5	5	2	24	24	2	5	5
2	A 1	1	2	25	25	25	1	1	25	11	2	2
13	U 17	17	9	13	12	15	17	18	13	12	19	21
13	T 14	11	20	2	3	26	14	13	13	22	2	L 13
2	22	26	1	9	18	21	22	21	8	22	11	15
24	25	14	25	1	5	12	19	3	17	23	11	7
25	13	13	25	11	R 7	2	11	4	22	4	22	7
11	1	8	21	15	19	16	1	11	14	15	7	1
2	11	25	13	19	9	2	14	11	1	13	25	18
22	14	13	1	14	4	18	18	22	4	26	11	13
2	2	24	17	10	16	26	19	6	10	22	6	4
10	9	15	6	11	13	2	12	22	F 18	18	1	12

16

The small grid is for ease of reference only.

Numbers	1	2	3	4	5	6	7	8	9	10	11	12	13
Letters													

Numbers	14	15	16	17	18	19	20	21	22	23	24	25	26
Letters													

The words to find in the grid are:

Autons
Auto-Plastic
Channing
Daffodils
Farrel
Hibbert
Killer Dolls

Master
Meteorites
Oxley Woods
Plastic
Phillips
Replicas
Rossini

6 The Yeti

All the answers to these questions can be placed in the grid on the following page. Answer the questions and fill in the grid. One letter has been filled in to help you.

1   It is the entity which controls the Yeti.
2   He helped the Doctor in both of his encounters with the Yeti.
3   Name of number 2's daughter.
4   Monastery attacked by the Yeti.
5   Holy relic from number 4 which was in the Doctor's possession.
6   The lama taken over by number 1.
7   He was the abbot of number 4.
8   He was the leader of the warrior monks of number 4.
9   There is one in every Yeti to make it function.
10 Number 1 took over this city using the Yeti.
11 Mountain range where number 4 can be found.
12 Name given to the defence buildings at Goodge Street Station.
13 Number 12's temporary CO before Colonel Lethbridge-Stewart arrived.
14 Soldier taken over by number 1 in number 10.
15 The reporter covering the Yeti invasion of number 10.
16 Doctor's companion captured by number 1 and used to blackmail the Doctor.
17 He was the driver of the truck trying to get ammunition to number 12.
18 He was number 8's guard captain.
19 Country in which number 4 can be found.
20 He destroyed number 1's link with Earth in number 19.

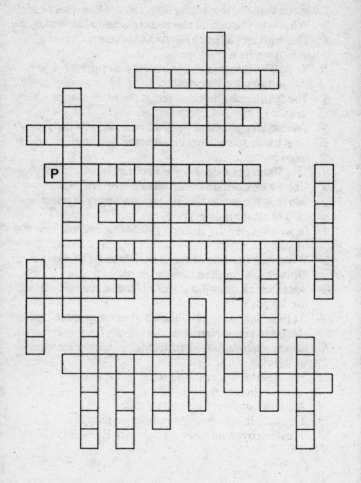

7 Milestones in the Doctor Who Saga

1   What was the title of the 50th *Doctor Who* story?
2   What was the title of the 100th *Doctor Who* story?
3   The 50th episode of *Doctor Who* occurred halfway through which story?
4   The 100th episode of *Doctor Who* occurred towards the end of which story?
5   The 200th episode occurred at the beginning of which story?
6   The 300th episode occurred at the end of which story?
7   The 400th episode occurred at the beginning of which story?
8   The 500th episode was the first part of which story?
9   The 600th episode occurred at the end of which story?
10 What number was the *Doctor Who* story in which the fifth Doctor made his debut?
11 In which story did the first Doctor regenerate into the second?
12 What was the title of the story in which the second Doctor regenerated into the third?
13 After which story did the third Doctor regenerate into the fourth?
14 At the conclusion of which story was the fourth Doctor forced to regenerate into the fifth?
15 In which story did the fifth Doctor regenerate into the sixth?

8 The Five Doctors

```
B A N A M O R T G D Y A T E S
O N T H E T O F E R T L S I T
Y E R F I L L A G I I L A S N
R M S Q P A D I Z Z L R R S A
E R K R V O T T S O A A A E S
W E H I E E O H R J T S H B U
O B A R Y T A C A H R U J N S
T Y R E U W S M S I O R A O Q
K C S I B K I A N E M O N L K
R N K D C E G G M O M B E I S
A D E A T H Z O N E I I S S I
D L L G J H G U O L R U T S L
E B A I E T E G A N A N D A E
H S D R O L E M I T O U T R B
T O M B Z R C O R O N E T T O
```

Here are the clues to the words that can be found in the grid:

1 The Doctor's race.
2 The home planet of number 1.
3 A forbidden area of number 2.
4 The one significant feature of the landscape of number 3.
5 The villain of *The Five Doctors*.
6 Number 1 sent him to help the Doctor.

7   She was trapped in the vortex with the fourth Doctor.

8   Companion of the first Doctor who was kidnapped.

9   One of the third Doctor's companions who was kidnapped.

10   It was the first thing the Doctor and number 8 met after they were re-united with each other.

11   The Chancellor of number 1 during this story.

12   He is reputed to be the greatest ever of number 1.

13   The _____ of number 12. It can be found in number 4.

14   Number 5 was seeking this.

15   It was used to kidnap the Doctors and various companions.

16   They were found in the Castellan's quarters but were incinerated.

17   She was the Doctor's current female companion at the time of this story.

18   He was the Doctor's other companion at the time of this story.

19   He accompanied the second Doctor throughout this story.

20   One of the third Doctor's female companions whom he encountered as an illusion.

21   A member of UNIT whom the Doctor met as an illusion.

22   One of the Doctor's male companions whom he met as an illusion.

23   The other female companion whom the Doctor met as an illusion.

24   _____ of number 12. It magnifies the power of someone's will.

25   _____ of number 12. it gives the wearer number 14.

26   The second Doctor and number 19 met one of these in some caves.

27   They tried to blow up the TARDIS with a bomb.

28   The form taken by the gateway into the vortex when it kidnapped the Doctors and their companions.

29   It was kidnapped along with the third Doctor.

9 Name That Date

The following anagrams each contain an anagram of a year during which the Doctor has visited Earth. Each year has been written out in full. The ten *Doctor Who* story titles written below the anagrams refer to the answers but have been muddled up.

1   S Y X T T I N I X S E
2   E E N L D D H V E U E T N N I D N R E N E A N E
3   X F T E N Y E I R I S N T U O E N
4   W S E R T Y O N A T T D D D F H N U X H N U Y O
    I D E S R O O U N A
5   Y I E T X S T X I I S S N E X
6   E H N D N I E T N D I E N N R E D N E N A N
7   H G H G Y E E N T E I N I E N T I E
8   V F Y E E N T T T I E I R I H N N E
9   F X I T N E S T E V Y R U E N E S O
10 Y E T N S N X X T I S I N E E I

The Time Meddler   *The Abominable Snowmen*
The Highlanders   *The Visitation*
The Faceless Ones   *The Talons of Weng-Chiang*
Planet of the Giants   *The Dalek Invasion of Earth*
The Pyramids of Mars   *The Horror of Fang Rock*

10 From One to Five

Place the answers to the following questions into the first of the two grids so that they read downwards. Then transfer the letters in the numbered squares into the appropriate squares on the second grid. If you are correct, the letters in the second grid will spell out the titles of six *Doctor Who* stories.

1   Most dangerous and addictive drug in the Universe.
2   Tegan's surname.
3   Double of Mary Tamm's Romana.
4   Title given to the leader of the people of Logopolis.
5   Planet of Aggedor.
6   Leader of the Gaztaks.
7   Creature which lived in the pit dug by the Daleks in Bedfordshire.
8   Name given to the human slaves under the control of the Daleks.
9   Planet with a living city.
10 Planet whose population is split into two groups known as the Savants and the Deons.
11 The first segment of the Key to Time was disguised as a lump of this.
12 They fought a war with the Argolin.
13 Planet devastated by the Nimon before Skonnos.
14 Vivien Fay's real name.
15 UNIT colonel in charge when the Kraals tried to invade Earth.
16 Scottish duke impersonated by Broton.

1	2	3	4	5	6	7	8	9	10	11	12	13	14	15	16
7		57		36		31		15	28		50	1	47	14	
	35	19	23			9	52		12						33
27	10	30	26		48					41		25	3	51	5
					34		37	55	21	20	24	53	46		
	13	38	54	22		42				16	2	29	8		
39			6	18	43	49	45	56	32		40	4			
		11						17					44		

1	2	3	4	5	6	7	8	9	10	11
12	13	14	15	16	17	18		19	20	21
22	23	24	25	26	27	28	29	30	31	
32	33	34	35	36	37	38	39	40		
41	42	43		44	45	46	47	48	49	
50	51	52	53	54	55	56	57			

11 Travelling in Space

This puzzle is a word search with a difference. Each different number represents a letter of the alphabet (with the same number always representing the same letter). For example the number 6 may turn out to be S so you would write an S in every square containing the number 6. Ten letters are given to you but working out the other sixteen is up to you.

19	5	19	23	1	15	18	6	25	17	15	22	25
22	10	17	7	3	15	23	3	25	16	13	3	17
21	19	26	25	6	22	15	17	23	20	21	25	4
19	24	23	12	17	11	4	1	1	14	E 17	1	17
25	17	4	17	19	17	5	3	15	7	25	15	19
2	2	26	4	19	1	20	18	13	15	O 3	9	16
8	17	22	7	15	17	19	19	6	3	17	2	15
12	9	12	13	1	15	26	20	19	5	S 19	19	17
21	1	U 26	4	16	17	23	16	6	17	A 1	19	4
17	23	15	15	23	1	15	D 13	I 6	19	B 5	2	3
7	17	12	13	23	22	16	8	25	6	Y 16	6	9
25	7	3	3	16	11	7	24	12	12	K 14	7	17
5	19	9	9	21	2	6	20	2	10	19	3	15

The small grid is for ease of reference only.

Numbers	1	2	3	4	5	6	7	8	9	10	11	12	13
Letters													

Numbers	14	15	16	17	18	19	20	21	22	23	24	25	26
Letters													

The words to find in the grid are:

P Seven E
Dynatrope
Empress
Hecate
Hydrax
Nerva
Probe Six
Probe Seven

Recovery Seven
Starliner
TARDIS
Sidrat
Terminus
Monarch's Ship
Skybase One

12 TLASENP

In each of the following cases the letters, once re-arranged, will spell out the name of a planet visited by the Doctor.

1 EKDALOAV
2 IRNPDOSI
3 TNARZIEMO
4 OSHCIRL
5 NOKSSON
6 GLASORI
7 LGETALI
8 HFLAROUZAT
9 RULAASZI
10 MTNIOEIRRN

13 Fourth's Success

All the following words can be found in the grid in a straight line either forwards, backwards, vertically, horizontally, or diagonally:

Meglos
Skagra
Xanxia
Oracle
Taren Capel
Styggron
Tryst
Shadow
Lady Adrasta
Cessair

The Collector
Eldrad
Sutekh
Davros
Scaroth
Count Grendel
Stor
Greel
Morbius
Broton

```
P L W O D A H S F S I G R T K
D C N V B R O T O N Q H L M X
Y A Q R E T S A M P Y W L O F
U T R A L J H O G C X S E R N
M S O C E S S A I R A C D B B
S A T P E T R A W B N A N I T
O R C G R D M H A N X R E U T
R D E T G Y E R F G I O R S N
V A L G F U G K E T A T G A O
A Y L I O A L G R C C H T H R
D D O G K S O Y W E G D N K G
Z A C S U U S T O R T S U E G
E L E E E T F E L C A R O T Y
R G H G H D A R D L E N C U T
D S T A R E N C A P E L D S S
```

14 Fourth's Stops

```
L  T  R  I  O  T  E  E  R  H
D  A  O  R  S  B  P  L  U  T
P  R  A  A  R  O  S  O  T  A
T  A  S  K  I  B  D  E  L  T
N  N  N  O  K  S  O  V  A  I
R  O  S  C  S  A  G  K  A  R
A  O  L  H  S  T  A  N  S  T
K  R  K  Z  R  I  T  E  Z  R
S  I  A  E  A  M  S  O  R  O
Z  A  N  T  A  M  I  N  O  T
```

If you track from letter to adjacent letter vertically or horizontally (no diagonals) on the grid, starting from the letter in the box, you can track out the names of sixteen planets visited by the fourth Doctor.

15 Doctor Who Abbreviations

What do all the following abbreviations stand for in *Doctor Who* terminology?

1	UNIT	11	TSS
2	TRG	12	TARDIS
3	IMC	13	SIDRAT
4	OMDSS	14	TOMTIT
5	WZO	15	CET
6	ICCA	16	APC
7	PCM	17	BOSS
8	MSC	18	CVE
9	HADS	19	WOTAN
10	WEB	20	SRS

16 The Adventures

All the answers to these questions can be placed in the grid on the following page. Answer the questions and fill in the grid; one letter has been filled in to help you.

1 Nyssa left the Doctor in this story.
2 Ian was made a knight in this story.
3 This story was never broadcast on television.
4 In this story the Master was finally arrested by UNIT.
5 The Cybermen attacked Earth through sewers in this story.
6 Adric stowed away in the TARDIS at the end of this story.
7 Nyssa slept right through this story.
8 In this story the Doctor gambled away the TARDIS.
9 In this story the Doctor had to defeat the Primords.
10 This was the fourth Doctor's first adventure.
11 Adric was killed in this story.
12 Ian and Barbara left the Doctor after this story.
13 In this story the Doctor helped the Gonds.
14 Adric was kidnapped by the Master in this story.
15 Vicki joined the Doctor in this story.
16 In this story the Doctor met the Minyans.
17 In this story Ian and Barbara were sold as slaves.
18 The sonic-screwdriver was destroyed in this story.
19 In this story the Doctor visited Tigella.
20 In this story the Doctor's life was saved by a Chumblie.
21 In this story the Mara was destroyed.
22 Steven left the Doctor in this story.
23 This was the fourth Doctor's last story.
24 In this story the TARDIS landed in a tomb.
25 In this story Tegan was briefly left behind by the Doctor.
26 In this story Dodo had a cold.
27 This was the Doctor's second adventure.

17 From First to Fifth

The following list contains the names of fifteen actors and actresses who have played the part of one of the Doctor's companions. Re-arrange the list so that it shows the order in which the companions they played joined the Doctor.

Elisabeth Sladen
Frazer Hines
Mark Strickson
Maureen O'Brien
Matthew Waterhouse
Carole Ann Ford
Mary Tamm
Jackie Lane

Janet Fielding
Wendy Padbury
Nicola Bryant
Katy Manning
Louise Jameson
Anneke Wills
Sarah Sutton

18 Hidden Stories

As well as being able to find all the following *Doctor Who* story titles in the word-search grid, you can also find six extra titles, one for each of the Doctors, by reading every unused letter on the finished grid from left to right as if they were in a book.

The titles to be found are:

Earthshock
Enlightenment
Frontios

Shada
Snakedance
Terminus

```
T T H E D A L E K S H E M R I
N S D T R O B B U E R T U H E
F O A N C E O N F S E O V I S
T I M E F L I G H T F L T H I
H T E M A M Z A T Y O E K C L
E N S N R T D H X N T C E T O
K O W E I A S A R H O N D I P
R R T T L O L E E H B E M M O
O F A H L A F A S T O H E S G
T E A G G N R H D E R V I L O
O S E I I K T H E C H A S E L
N M E L C R I C L L U F T H E
S A S N A K E D A N C E W A K
E T H E F I V E D O C T O R S
N I S N O M E D S G N I K N G
```

19 TOOCRD HOW VLENSO

In each of the following cases the letters, once re-arranged, will show the title of a *Doctor Who* adventure novelised by Terrance Dicks.

1 TSDAEYOTACEF
2 OYRFOMDUTSAODO
3 NLLEFPVTAIOE
4 FONHNMOSNRIO
5 RRIFMYPAASMODS
6 AFENOAHRFD
7 BVELNNMSIIYEIE
8 VSODIANRNIDOANI
9 SDOFTABOHETOR
10 CLFEVFAIOE

20 Bringing in UNIT

Re-arrange this list of *Doctor Who* stories featuring UNIT so that they are in chronological order.

The Day of the Daleks
The Ambassadors of Death
The Green Death
The Terror of the Autons
Robot
The Time Monster
Spearhead from Space
The Three Doctors
Invasion of the Dinosaurs
Claws of Axos

The Invasion
Terror of the Zygons
Inferno
The Daemons
The Android Invasion
The Time Warrior
Planet of the Spiders
The Mind of Evil
The Silurians

21 Fifth's Enemies

If you track from letter to adjacent letter vertically or horizontally (no diagonals) on the grid, starting from the letter in the box, you can track out the names of eleven enemies encountered by the fifth Doctor.

S	N	A	I	Y	K	G	E	E	T
P	W	D	R	U	S	A	M	E	L
M	A	R	Y	L	I	S	O	P	I
R	E	T	N	B	A	L	I	T	R
D	B	S	U	R	N	N	S	T	E
A	L	A	D	R	K	A	C	A	L
N	S	M	I	A	U	G	K	F	B
R	E	N	A	N	S	C	N	M	A
E	T	S	M	O	B	Y	E	A	R
P	L	A	A	T	E	R	M	H	D

22 Odd-One-Out

In each of the following cases there is one odd item: which is the odd one out, and why?

1   Zygons, Silurians, Movellans, Humans, Daleks, Shrievenzale, Exxilon, Rutans.
2   America, England, Wales, Scotland, Japan, China, Egypt, and Italy.
3   Earth, Spiridon, Ribos, Exxilon, Mechanus, Kembel, Aridius, Skaro.
4   Ribos, Atrios, Voga, Zeos, Earth, Zanak, Delta Three, Callufrax.
5   Nyssa, Barbara, Ian, Susan, Steven, Adric, Vicki, Perpugilliam.
6   *Castrovalva*, *The Sea Devils*, *The King's Demons*, *Arc of Infinity*, *The Time Meddler*, *Meglos*, *The War Games*, *The Brain of Morbius*.
7   *The Five Doctors*, *The Three Doctors*, *The Ambassadors of Death*, *Arc of Infinity*, *Logopolis*, *The Mutants*, *The Sea Devils*, *Meglos*.
8   Cybermen, Daleks, Nestenes, Kraals, Wirrn, Krynoids, Visians, Axons.
9   *The Daleks*, *The Keys of Marinus*, *The Dalek Invasion of Earth*, *The Krotons*, *The Android Invasion*, *Genesis of the Daleks*, *The Chase*, *Mission to the Unknown*.
10 Daleks, Kraals, Krotons, Cybermen, Dominators, Yeti, Chameleons, the Macra.

23 Find That Planet

```
D M K E S C T T L L E B M E K
W U V O U R Y S O P Q T A D S
B I L R A T O S C L M K U Z I
V O H K J B Z L N U W V A A L
S C E M I C E K G T Q G L I O
K N E R S S T R N O D A L E P
A O N T X J A U E A D L E B O
R O U N N N M M T C K L G D G
O Z S P I R I D O N W I I Z O
T A X V C P N Z R A M F T V L
M A R S S O O Z Z U P R I O N
R A P T M A R I N U S E A R X
S K O N N O S X I T O Y O T U
S U I R A Z L A M E T A R I M
A V L A V O R T S A C E T S S
```

All these words can be found in the grid in straight lines including diagonally:

Dulkis	Castrovalva
Solos	Mars
Spiridon	Pluto
Tigella	Vortis
Peladon	Gallifrey
Zeta Minor	Skonnos
Skaro	Mira
Marinus	Kembel
Traken	Alzarius
Logopolis	Ribos

24 Set Down

Match each of the following planets with the story in which the Doctor visited it.

	The Planets	**The Stories**
1	Aridius	*Kinda*
2	Atrios	*The Pirate Planet*
3	Delta Three	*Carnival of Monsters*
4	Deva Loka	*Snakedance*
5	Dulkis	*The Chase*
6	Exarius	*Meglos*
7	Exxilon	*Planet of the Daleks*
8	Frontios	*The Brain of Morbius*
9	Inter Minor	*The Dominators*
10	Karn	*Tomb of the Cybermen*
11	Manussa	*The Power of Kroll*
12	Metebelis Three	*Destiny of the Daleks*
13	Oseidon	*Planet of Evil*
14	Pluto	*The Green Death*
15	Skaro	*Colony in Space*
16	Spiridon	*The Android Invasion*
17	Telos	*The Sunmakers*
18	Zanak	*Death to the Daleks*
19	Zeta Minor	*The Armageddon Factor*
20	Zolfa-Thura	Fifth Doctor story of the same title

25 The Loyal Companions

T	Y	S	S	N	A	D	R	J	Z
W	N	B	A	O	S	V	I	J	O
A	H	E	A	C	K	L	C	A	G
Z	S	N	J	O	D	E	E	L	R
I	Y	A	T	H	E	T	O	P	A
L	L	F	N	E	V	S	L	T	N
R	O	J	O	V	K	A	L	Y	I
Y	T	N	F	A	N	E	O	Z	K
T	G	A	O	D	O	D	E	T	C
T	E	I	C	H	A	P	L	V	I

If you track from letter to adjacent letter vertically or horizontally (no diagonals) on the above grid, starting from the letter in the box, you can track out the names of twelve of the Doctors' companions.

26 Name That Planet

1 The Doctor met Omega in this story:
   A *Arc of Infinity*
   B *Terminus*
   C *The Armageddon Factor*
   D *Inferno*
   E *The Invasion of Time*
2 The Doctor met the Master in this story:
   K *Shada*
   L *The Green Death*
   M *The Leisure Hive*
   N *Nightmare of Eden*
   O *Time-Flight*
3 The Doctor had to defeat BOSS in this story:
   P *The War Machines*
   Q *The Doomsday Weapon*
   R *The Robots of Death*
   S *The Green Death*
   T *The Seeds of Doom*
4 The Doctor's opponent in this story was Taren Capel:
   P *The Talons of Weng-Chiang*
   Q *Planet of the Giants*
   R *The Robots of Death*
   S *The Green Death*
   T *The Daemons*
5 Magnus Greel was the Doctor's opponent in:
   K *The Talons of Weng-Chiang*
   L *The Mind of Evil*
   M *The Doomsday Weapon*
   N *The Daemons*
   O *Shada*

Once you have what you believe to be the five correct answers, take the letter representing each answer (if you think the answer to number 5 is Shada you would take the letter O) and re-arrange them to form the name of a planet visited by the Doctor on several occasions.

27 Aliens in Hiding

```
A S O B D R A H V I N S D X V
R N N F I P U V W G Q M K Y S
N O S O Z C O L S J O N M T R
H R E C E O A N K N R E P Q O
M E G U R L A D O N H M Z Z I
O X J D L I E I X T S R A O R
R M S A C I D M W N S E R I R
O Y B L M S T V A E F B B B A
K N U E A Y M E S H D Y I V W
S D X K C I T R Y G C C H E E
P W F S R N A S N O T O R K C
O U S N A E N O D I D L C K I
R I L L S S E N S O R I T E S
J T T Z F R E F U S I A N S H
N A R E T P O N E M U Y I J O
```

All of the following aliens can be found in the grid:

Atlanteans
Chameleons
Cybermen
Daleks
Didoneans
Drahvins
Dulcians
Ice Warriors
Krotons
Macra

Menoptera
Monoids
Moroks
Refusians
Rills
Sensorites
Voords
Xerons
Yeti
Zarbi

44

28 The Ice Warriors

All the answers to these questions can be placed in the grid on the following page. Answer the questions and fill in the grid: one letter has been filled in to help you.

1   They attempted to take over the Earth on two occasions but later reformed.
2   It is the planet of origin of number 1.
3   He was the leader of number 1 trapped in prehistoric ice.
4   The Doctor used it to destroy number 3 and his crew.
5   Planet other than Earth visited by number 1.
6   Mineral found in abundance on number 5.
7   He was the ambassador of number 1 to number 5.
8   He was number 7's assistant.
9   Number 7 was an agent for this group.
10 They emit a lethal fungus.
11 Number 10 arrived on Earth by way of this.
12 He led the invasion attempt on Earth using number 10.
13 It went to war with number 9.
14 He betrayed number 9 to number 13 for money.
15 Miners' leader on number 5.
16 He helped number 14 betray number 9 to number 13.
17 He was number 3's second-in-command.
18 He was number 14's henchman.
19 Number 1 were planning to launch an attack on Earth from here.
20 It destroyed number 1 on number 19.

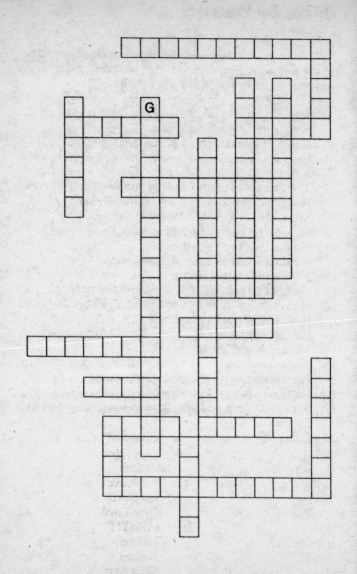

29 Master-Plan

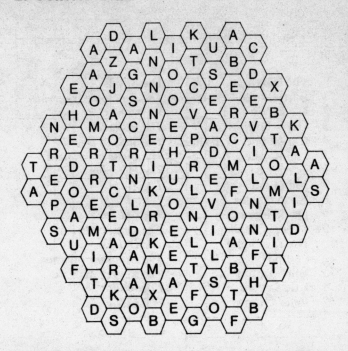

Each of the following twenty words connected with the Master can be found in the hexagonal grid by tracking from a letter to one of the six adjoining letters in a straight line.

Atlantis
Autons
Axos
Azal
Bok
Concorde
Evil
Exarius
Goth
Kalid

Kamelion
King John
Melkur
Portreeve
Sea Devils
Time Lord
TOMTIT
Traken
Tremas
Xeraphin

30 The Novels

Match each of the following Doctor Who novelists with their respective novels.

	The Novelists	The Novels
1	Barry Letts	*The Sontaran Experiment*
2	David Whitaker	*Warriors' Gate*
3	Gerry Davis	*The Visitation*
4	Christopher H. Bidmead	*The State of Decay*
5	Ian Marter	*The Curse of Peladon*
6	Terrance Dicks	*The Daemons*
7	John Lydecker	*The Zarbi*
8	Brian Hayles	*Time-Flight*
9	David Fisher	*The Cybermen*
10	Malcolm Hulke	*The Leisure Hive*
11	Andrew Smith	*The Daleks*
12	Philip Hinchcliffe	*The Dinosaur Invasion*
13	Bill Strutton	*The Keys of Marinus*
14	Eric Saward	*Logopolis*
15	Peter Grimwade	*Full Circle*

31 Exterminate! Exterminate!

A	L	E	K	S	T	H	A	L	E
D	I	V	E	A	J	E	D	M	K
E	L	O	E	D	L	L	P	A	S
H	T	F	H	H	T	A	R	E	T
E	U	M	T	T	A	N	L	A	D
S	E	H	T	O	E	D	E	K	E
U	D	A	L	S	T	S	P	S	H
M	A	P	E	K	H	E	A	O	T
E	C	S	R	A	W	E	C	S	E
T	H	E	T	H	E	C	H	A	X

If you track from letter to adjacent letter vertically or horizontally (no diagonals) on the grid starting from the letter in the box, you can track out the titles of seven *Doctor Who* stories featuring the Daleks.

32 Name That Enemy

1 He died trying to save Earth:
   A Adric
   B Ian Chesterton
   C Harry Sullivan
   D Steven Taylor
   E Ben Jackson

2 This member of the TARDIS crew was an American botany student:
   K Nyssa
   L Sarah Jane Smith
   M Tegan Jovanka
   N Jo Grant
   O Perpugilliam Brown

3 This member of the TARDIS crew left the Doctor to lead an alien race:
   F Polly
   G Steven Taylor
   H Ben Jackson
   I Zoe Herriot
   J Dodo Chaplet

4 The amplified screams of this companion actually destroyed a monster:
   A Sarah Jane Smith
   B Jo Grant
   C Barbara Wright
   D Tegan Jovanka
   E Victoria Waterfield

5 This companion briefly caught Lazars' disease:
   K Victoria Waterfield
   L Tegan Jovanka
   M Nyssa
   N Turlough
   O Susan

Once you have what you believe to be the five correct answers, take the letter representing each answer (if you think the answer to number 5 is Turlough you would take the letter N) and re-arrange them to form the name of one of the Doctor's most powerful enemies. Who is the enemy and in which stories did the Doctor meet him?

33 HET PNSOMAOICN

The letters below hide the names of ten of the Doctor's companions. Re-arrange all the letters in each line to find the first names and surnames.

1 NYELVRTTOAES
2 MNAJHRSEATIHAS
3 HBIATARWRAGBR
4 KNOCEJNBSA
5 VTNNJAKOAEGA
6 ENHEROCTASTNI
7 DROAKAMGSNI
8 URVIHLASNYLAR
9 CIMEMAOMCJMINR
10 FTDAEVEILOWIRCAITR

34 Do You Know Your Doctor Who Facts?

All the answers to the following questions can be placed in the grid in the same order in a spiral pattern, starting in the direction of the arrow. Each of the answers overlaps the previous one by one or two letters.

1 British detective who helped the Doctor defeat Scaroth.
2 He was leader of the Sevateem.
3 It was the computer in charge of the *P7E*.
4 Colonist on the planet Exarius who was killed by the IMC robot.
5 Proctor of Traken.
6 Planet that paid tribute to Skonnos.
7 Scientist in charge of the refinery on Delta Three.
8 Companion of the Doctor and daughter of Tremas.
9 Leader of the second Morestran expedition to Zeta Minor.
10 Planet of the Leisure Hive.
11 Ex-partner and prisoner of the space pirate Caven.
12 Planet which is a member of the Cyrrenic Alliance.
13 Planet of the Kraals.
14 Leader of the crew of Nerva who was taken over by the Wirrn.
15 Chief of King Zargo's guards.
16 Sontaran who was conducting experiments on humans.
17 A sophisticated Auton which can pass for a human.
18 She was originally known as Navigation Officer Lauren Macmillan of the *Hydrax*.
19 The Tharil who rescued his race from the clutches of Rorvic.
20 One of the Deciders of Alzarius.
21 Project to penetrate the Earth's crust to collect Stahlman's Gas.
22 It took the Doctor's first three regenerations to defeat him.

23 Queen of Atlantis and wife of Dalios.
24 Companion of the Doctor who was killed trying to save the Earth.

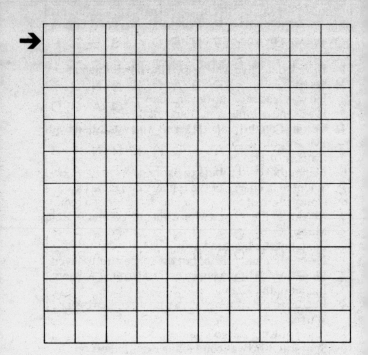

35 All About The Time Lords

```
O N T L H A D N E F H E F I C
C A S T E L L A N R S T M P A
O N H D A Y T N E D I S E R P
O F O T H E M O N T S E S Y I
H N B O V A R D A N S N N D T
F V O R T E X S A X A O A O O
P R G C I L I R X E M Z Y N L
T H A Q I D A I C R E H N I B
O U N R R T R G A T O T I A F
M E S A N T P H U A N A M N G
I N T O A W F O H R I E C S H
T H S M E O A U N P A D A H S
T H O R E O A R C A L I A N C
T H E Y R O M A N C P E O F T
G R E A T V A M P I R E H E R
```

The words to find in the grid are:

Arcalian
Capitol
Castellan
CIA
Death Zone
Eye of Harmony
Fendahl
Great Vampire
Matrix
Minyans

Panopticon
President
Prydonians
Shada
Shobogans
Sontarans
TARDIS
Vardans
Vortex

36 Know Your Storyline?

Match each of the following *Doctor Who* story titles with the main enemy the Doctor had to defeat.

	The Stories	**The Enemies**
1	*The Talons of Weng-Chiang*	BOSS
2	*Shada*	The Great Intelligence
3	*The Hand of Fear*	Omega
4	*Castrovalva*	Scaroth
5	*The Time Warrior*	Eldrad
6	*City of Death*	Taren Capel
7	*The Robots of Death*	Oracle
8	*The Web Planet*	Linx
9	*The Green Death*	The Giant Vampire
10	*The Pyramids of Mars*	The Master
11	*Underworld*	The Animus
12	*Arc of Infinity*	Sutekh
13	*State of Decay*	Forester
14	*The Web of Fear*	Magnus Greel
15	*Planet of Giants*	Skagra

37 The Cybermen

All the answers to the following questions can be placed in the grid on the following page. Answer the questions and fill in the grid; one letter has been filled in for you.

1   Humans that turned themselves into cyborgs.
2   It was Earth's sister planet.
3   Number 2 drained this from Earth.
4   It was located in the Moonbase in 2070.
5   Number 1 are alergic to this element.
6   It is called the planet of number 5.
7   The tombs of number 1 are located on this planet.
8   They home in on brain activity.
9   He plotted with number 1 on number 7.
10   She helped number 9.
11   Number 1 planned to use it as a base to attack number 6.
12   The Doctor, Jamie and Zoe helped defend it from number 1.
13   It was found on the rocket orbiting number 12.
14   It was used by number 1 to paralyse the population of Earth.
15   He built number 14.
16   He forced number 15 to build number 14.
17   Number 1 attacked a paralysed Earth through these.
18   He introduced number 8 to number 11.
19   Number 1 were going to use three of these to destroy number 6.
20   A group of them were destroyed by androids belonging to number 1 on 25th century Earth.
21   Number 1 were directly responsible for his death on a 25th century spaceship.
22   Number 1 used one to try to break into the bridge of the ship in previous question.
23   She was captain of the ship in question 21.

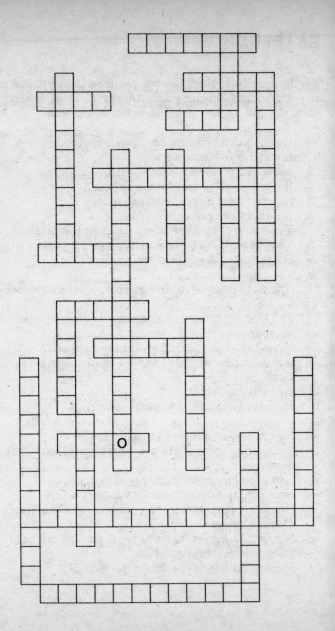

38 The Stars

Match each of the following stars with the main *Doctor Who* characters they have played.

	The Stars	The Characters
1	Frazer Hines	Jo Grant
2	Deborah Watling	Ben Jackson
3	Ian Marter	Perpugilliam Brown
4	Maureen O'Brien	Harry Sullivan
5	Carole Ann Ford	The Brigadier
6	Janet Fielding	Turlough
7	William Russell	Romana (first incarnation)
8	Katy Manning	Jamie McCrimmon
9	Nicholas Courtney	Polly
10	Sarah Sutton	Tegan Jovanka
11	Jacqueline Hill	Benton
12	Michael Craze	Ian Chesterton
13	Peter Purves	Zoe Herriot
14	John Levene	Sarah Jane Smith
15	Matthew Waterhouse	Steven Taylor
16	Jean Marsh	Victoria Waterfield
17	Richard Franklin	Captain Yates
18	Mary Tamm	Barbara Wright
19	Mark Strickson	Sara Kingdom
20	Elisabeth Sladen	Vicki
21	Jackie Lane	Liz Shaw
22	Louise Jameson	Romana (second incarnation)
23	Nicola Bryant	Nyssa
24	Wendy Padbury	Dodo Chaplet
25	Lalla Ward	Susan
26	Adrienne Hill	Adric
27	Anneke Wills	Leela
28	Caroline John	Katarina

39 The Sontarans

This puzzle is a word search with a difference. Each different number represents a letter of the alphabet (with the same number always representing the same letter). For example, the number 19 may turn out to be T so you would write a T in every square containing the number 19. Ten letters are given to you but working out the other sixteen is up to you.

11	26	2	14	4	2	V 23	1	C 13	5	10	22
12	25	14	Y 18	2	26	8	25	15	15	5	5
20	18	16	2	26	25	O 10	I 25	13	1	1	11
2	11	25	5	25	26	10	4	14	26	10	4
1	7	9	2	15	N 4	E 2	R 26	A 1	11	1	8
7	22	4	4	4	11	5	11	15	13	23	2
7	11	23	10	3	19	4	15	5	14	26	13
12	4	25	15	21	10	1	18	2	26	19	25
13	2	22	13	5	20	11	3	13	10	1	7
21	4	1	25	15	15	U 17	26	2	11	4	10
2	2	11	25	1	2	26	18	11	5	5	26
5	5	2	18	2	9	11	1	2	26	14	16

The small grid is for ease of reference only.

Numbers	1	2	3	4	5	6	7	8	9	10	11	12	13
Letters													

Numbers	14	15	16	17	18	19	20	21	22	23	24	25	26
Letters													

The words to find in the grid are:

Clones
Gallifrey
Galsec
Great Key
Hal
Hyperioi
Irongron
Kelner
Linx

Probic Vent
Rutans
Scavenger
Sontara
Stor
Styre
Terullian
Vardans

40 Mystery Companion

1   In which story did the Doctor regenerate from the first
    Doctor into the second?
    A   *The Tenth Planet*
    B   *The War Machines*
    C   *The Dalek Masterplan*
    D   *The War Games*
    E   *The Savages*

2   In which story did the Doctor regenerate from the
    second Doctor into the third?
    A   *The Invasion*
    B   *The Planet of the Spiders*
    C   *The Krotons*
    D   *The Highlanders*
    E   *The War Games*

3   In which story did the Doctor regenerate from the
    third Doctor into the fourth?
    F   *Invasion of the Dinosaurs*
    G   *The Planet of the Spiders*
    H   *Death to the Daleks*
    I   *Day of the Daleks*
    J   *The War Games*

4   In which story did the Doctor regenerate from the
    fourth Doctor into the fifth?
    K   *The Horns of Nimon*
    L   *The Keeper of Traken*
    M   *The Android Invasion*
    N   *Logopolis*
    O   *Castrovalva*

5   In which story did the Doctor regenerate from the fifth
    Doctor into the sixth?
    P   *Arc of Infinity*
    Q   *Enlightenment*
    R   *The Visitation*
    S   *Snakedance*
    T   *The Caves of Androzani*

Once you have what you believe to be the five correct answers, take the letter representing each answer (if you think the answer to number 5 is *Snakedance* you would take the letter S and re-arrange them to form the name of one of the Doctor's companions. Who is the companion and in which story did he/she make his/her last major appearance?

41 Ugh! What Is It?

Y	B	E	R	N	M	I	M	O	N
C	S	K	M	E	O	N	A	R	T
S	D	E	Y	E	V	S	N	A	Y
L	A	L	L	L	K	R	N	T	T
I	T	P	A	B	S	A	O	S	H
S	T	E	N	O	N	R	G	S	O
N	E	L	S	G	M	S	S	E	N
O	R	I	D	Y	Z	E	T	T	I
T	O	A	R	G	S	N	R	I	A
K	R	S	H	I	B	S	O	S	N

If you track from letter to adjacent letter vertically or horizontally (no diagonals) on the grid, starting from the letter in the box, you can track out the names of twelve non-human species which the Doctor has met.

42 The Doctor vs. The Master

In each of the anagrammatical lines below is hidden the name of an actor who has played either the part of the Doctor or the Master.

1 OKRTAMBE
2 RREPTAPTET
3 GTCOPUKHORNITTAR
4 EHLYANNIYTNAO
5 LROEKNABIC
6 GGOOAEDRDLRE
7 SEDNVOEPIRAT
8 ITLNRLWLMHAALEI
9 VFEBYEEGSEFRROE
10 WNETOPJERE

43 Mystery Story

Each of the answers to the following fourteen questions are *Doctor Who* story titles. When you have answered all the questions, take the initial letter from each answer (if the answer starts with 'The' ignore the T and use the initial letter of the next word) and re-arrange them to form the title of another story. What is the mystery story?

1   Adric was killed in this story.
2   The Master hi-jacked two Concordes in this story.
3   The Cybermen allied themselves with Tobias Vaughn in this story.
4   In this story the Doctor had to defeat the last Zolfa-Thuran.
5   This was Turlough's third story.
6   In this story the Master was arrested by UNIT.
7   In this story the Doctor had to defeat both the Silurians and the Sea Devils.
8   The randomiser was destroyed in this story.
9   In this story the Doctor met the Black Guardian for the first time.
10 Nyssa left the Doctor in this story.
11 This story took place during the Second Ice Age.
12 Turlough joined the Doctor in this story.
13 In this story the Doctor met the Mandrels.
14 In this story the Doctor visited Skonnos.

44 Planet Search

```
S I R I S O R E T S E A H P E
N Q S K F A C R H K L Y T I D
G U A N G A M A T L E D T O V
J R L Z A R A T N O S X E P W
O M Z B S Q E P F T D W N S A
A I A Y N L E E B E X S A A Z
R V R S R D U L V O J U L H O
I C I U E K G A P H M I P P S
M D U N F L L D H K R D H I E
D S S I M O V O A P I I T R I
B Z R R K N J N C I B R F E D
R U T A T H R E E T O A I X O
Y J X M M S W O Q V S G F E N
R F S E N S E S P H E R E B N
R M E T E B E L I S T H R E E
```

Hidden in the grid are the names of the home planets of each of the following species:

1	Aggedor	11	Osirians
2	Daleks	12	Rutans
3	The Fendahl	13	Sensorites
4	Giant Spiders	14	Shrievenzale
5	Ice Warriors	15	Sontarans
6	Kinda	16	Swampies
7	Kraals	17	Visians
8	Mandrels	18	Voords
9	Marshmen	19	Xeraphin
10	Mire Beasts	20	Zarbi

45 Planet Choice

1   The Doctor fought him on Zolfa-Thura:
    A   Kelner
    B   Zabec
    C   Master
    D   Stael
    E   Meglos

2   He was the detective who helped the Doctor and
    Romana defeat Scaroth:
    L   Mitchell
    M   Duggan
    N   Morgan
    O   Fisk
    P   Porter

3   It was the robot investigator on the Sandminer:
    A   SV7
    B   D84
    C   V6
    D   D12
    E   D63

4   He was the second Doctor's double:
    A   Tobias Vaughn
    B   The War Chief
    C   Kleig
    D   Grey
    E   Salamander

5   Guerillas from the 22nd century wanted to kill him:
    J   Professor Horner
    K   Bill Filer
    L   Styles
    M   The Doctor
    N   The Brigadier

6   He was the Keeper of the Concience of Marinus:
    J   Autloc
    K   Arbitan
    L   Zentos
    M   Tegana
    N   Maaga

Once you have got what you believe to be the six correct
answers, take the letter representing each answer (if you
think the answer to number 6 is Maaga you would take the
letter N) and re-arrange them to form the name of a planet
visited by the first Doctor; what is the planet and what
happened to it?

46 The Daleks

All of the answers to the following questions can be placed in the grid on the following page. Answer the questions and fill in the grid; one letter has been filled in for you.

1   They are the most evil creatures in the universe.
2   It was the supreme weapon of number 1.
3   It was the mineral which powered number 2.
4   He created number 1.
5   Most of them were massacred by number 1.
6   They were at war with number 5.
7   He offered number 3 to number 1.
8   It was ravaged by number 2.
9   It is the home planet of number 1.
10 There was a living city here.
11 Number 1 went to number 10 for this.
12 He was an SSSS agent and was killed on number 8 by number 1.
13 This species work for number 1.
14 It almost occurred between Earth and Draconia.
15 He helped number 1 conceive number 14.
16 They are at war with number 1.
17 Number 1 had a vast frozen army stationed here.
18 The Doctor used one to re-freeze the army on number 17.
19 He was a number 5, met the Doctor on number 17 and was killed by number 1.
20 This colony thought they could control number 1.
21 The deformed bodies of number 6 travel around in these.
22 Mire Beasts live here.
23 He helped number 1 but was left stranded on an ice planet by the Doctor.

47 The Companions

Match each of the following companions with the story in which they first met the Doctor.

	The Companions	The Stories
1	Adric	*Robot*
2	Dodo	*The War Machines*
3	Harry	*Spearhead from Space*
4	Jamie	*The Ribos Operation*
5	Jo	*The Face of Evil*
6	Katarina	*The Invisible Enemy*
7	K9	*The King's Demons*
8	Kamelion	*Terror of the Autons*
9	Leela	*The Time Warrior*
10	Liz	*The Myth Makers*
11	Nyssa	*The Massacre*
12	Perpugilliam	*The Chase*
13	Polly	*The Highlanders*
14	Romana	*The Evil of the Daleks*
15	Sarah Jane	*The Rescue*
16	Steven	*The Wheel in Space*
17	Tegan	*The Keeper of Traken*
18	Victoria	*Full Circle*
19	Vicki	*Logopolis*
20	Zoe	*Planet of Fire*

48 UNIT

This puzzle is a word search with a difference. Each different number represents a letter of the alphabet (with the same number always representing the same letter). For example, if the number 21 turned out to be V, you would write the letter V in every square containing the number 21.

						O	I	R						L
19	3	22	25	7	12	18	3	12	24	21	23	18	2	23
14	14	6	19	24	19	3	1	7	1	21	1	12	A 1	9
22	15	19	12	2	23	23	2	17	12	1	2	2	19	21
1	18	12	19	11	1	3	12	6	23	3	19	18	20	25
8	16	5	19	22	14	1	25	3	21	20	1	2	15	18
11	2	2	12	2	1	2	21	1	23	2	17	19	9	8
9	3	21	4	23	11	22	16	15	1	2	25	25	19	18
11	2	12	19	18	2	3	9	9	3	4	21	7	18	12
21	12	2	25	8	12	4	25	6	1	11	26	23	11	25
5	19	11	13	8	19	19	25	19	11	2	19	2	18	11
2	2	12	24	11	2	12	25	1	2	12	2	19	12	1
8	25	25	18	25	2	2	23	9	18	11	19	2	17	3
22	1	16	25	25	12	2	8	1	22	18	24	23	1	16
15	7	8	2	12	4	2	11	22	26	25	3	20	10	10
14	2	22	19	11	18	M 4	2	1	21	26	5	1	6	10

73

The small grid is for ease of reference only.

Numbers	1	2	3	4	5	6	7	8	9	10	11	12	13
Letters													

Numbers	14	15	16	17	18	19	20	21	22	23	24	25	26
Letters													

The words to find in the grid are:

Axos
Azal
Benton
BOSS
Brigadier
Cybermen
Daemons
Daleks
Faraday
Giant Robot

Kraals
Kronos
Master
Old Priory
Omega
Silurians
Styles
Yates
Zygons

49 Track-a-Story

I	M	E	L	C	R	I	L	U	F
T	E	F	L	M	S	C	L	C	E
A	V	L	I	G	H	T	S	N	A
A	S	A	V	J	E	S	N	A	D
C	T	R	O	R	A	I	L	K	E
K	H	S	H	T	H	A	O	P	D
C	O	X	U	S	S	D	A	O	Y
Z	M	I	N	H	G	N	E	G	O
H	R	N	E	T	I	L	G	L	L
T	E	M	E	N	T	M	E	O	S

If you track from letter to adjacent letter vertically or horizontally (no diagonals) on the grid, starting from the letter in the box, you can track out the titles of ten adventures of the fourth and fifth Doctors.

50 Aliens vs. The Doctor

Re-arrange this mixed-up list of aliens so that they are in the order in which the Doctor first met them.

Chameleons
Cybermen
Daemons
Daleks
Dominators
Drahvins
Eternals
Giant Spiders
Ice Warriors
Kraals
Krotons
Krynoids
Macra

Nimon
Primords
Sea Devils
Silurians
Sontarans
Terileptils
Urbankans
Voords
Wirrn
Yeti
Zarbi
Zygons

51 Time Search

```
K T U C A D R E M O G A T H I
W L S U I B R O M F R B U I V
J R F G O T H E Y S B M K L E
P J S P F E G U K O I R T D R
X L N Z M A Q O R M P A C R E
P A R L V A S U T R N S H E N
K Y E O P U S F O B R S L D L
F P N F X A T T C Y X I L K E
I E G C A V C F E Z R L E U K
N I I C R O R D A R K O R K X
I S N H D D J T B G N N D K O
D H C O C L X N A D O R N M V
E C O B S R R L V T M X A P H
H J G N I V A Y L A S M P K A
A N D R E D F W I Z W U S D Y
```

All the following words can be found in the grid:

Doctor	Kelner
Master	Salyavin
Omega	Spandrell
War Chief	Borusa
Monk	Rodan
Morbius	Andred
Rassilon	Gomer
Drax	Engin
K'anpo	Hildred
Goth	Hedin

52 Number 5 vs. Omega

This puzzle is a word search with a difference. Each different number represents a letter of the alphabet (with the same number always representing the same letter). For example, if the number 10 turned out to be P, you would write the letter P in every square containing the number 10. Ten letters are given to you but working out the other sixteen is up to you.

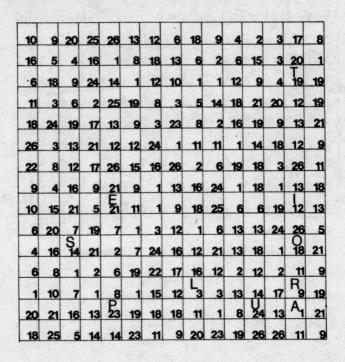

The small grid is for ease of reference only.

Numbers	1	2	3	4	5	6	7	8	9	10	11	12	13
Letters													

Numbers	14	15	16	17	18	19	20	21	22	23	24	25	26
Letters													

The words to find in the grid are:

Arc of Infinity
Amsterdam
Bio Data
Bonding
Borusa
Colin
Crypt
Damon
Ergon
Fusion Booster

Gallifrey
Hedin
Matrix
Maxil
Matter-Converter
Robin
Talor
Tegan
Thalia
Zorac

53 Featuring the Dalek!

Re-arrange this list of *Doctor Who* stories featuring the Daleks so that they are in the order in which they occurred on television.

The Evil of the Daleks
Frontier in Space
The Dalek Masterplan
The Space Museum
Resurrection of the Daleks
Day of the Daleks
The Daleks
The Power of the Daleks

Planet of the Daleks
Mission to the Unknown
Destiny of the Daleks
The Chase
Genesis of the Daleks
Death to the Daleks
The Dalek Invasion of Earth
The Five Doctors

54 Alien Attack

S	N	W	Z	S	N	E	N	E	T
M	O	G	Y	T	A	S	A	X	S
A	N	A	K	U	N	A	R	O	E
R	D	R	R	R	S	T	A	S	N
A	G	O	Y	A	L	N	O	S	S
D	I	O	N	A	S	I	C	E	N
S	W	I	R	R	K	I	R	W	O
L	E	K	R	O	N	O	R	A	E
A	C	S	N	K	E	R	H	A	L
D	Y	B	E	R	M	S	C	M	E

If you track from letter to adjacent letter vertically or horizontally (no diagonals) on the grid, starting from the letter in the box, you can track out the names of thirteen alien species which have tried to invade Earth.

The Answers

1 So You Think You Know About Who? – page 10

1 *Fury from the Deep*
2 It is a type forty.
3 The Daleks
4 It was Professor Kettlewell's robot.
5 It is the prison planet of the Time Lords.
6 It was a stage play written by Terrance Dicks and featuring Trevor Martin as the Doctor.
7 Kasteroborous
8 Theta Sigma
9 Ten, zero, eleven, zero zero by zero two
10 *The Tenth Planet*
11 The Isop Galaxy
12 Argolis
13 Monarch, Enlightenment and Persuasion
14 Andromeda
15 Patrex – Heliotrope; Arcalian – Green; Prydonians – Orange and scarlet
16 An atomic shell hit his laboratory, shattering his body so he built himself a mobile life-support system.
17 Cyclo Vybe Transmitter
18 King John
19 It was the computer at the Britannicus Base during the Second Ice Age.
20 Triple Alpha
21 Jaffa
22 Parrinium
23 740
24 It means 'A fly caught in honey'.
25 A Tachyon Generator
26 It is like that of a cactus.
27 The New Heidelberg University
28 'Entropy Increases'.
29 It was the sequence for checking the seals on a Starfall Seven spacesuit, an operation their ancestors often performed.

30 Occhinos
31 *Metropolitan*
32 Zeos
33 Cambridge
34 On Saturday, 23 November 1963 at 5.25 pm (ten minutes later than its scheduled time).
35 John Nathan-Turner

2 Robots, Robots, Everywhere – page 12

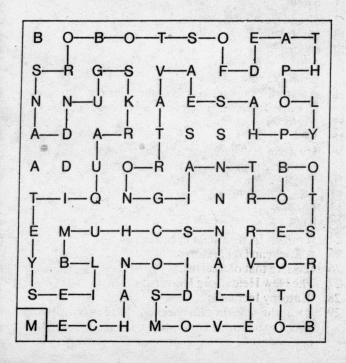

Mechonoids	Gundans
Movellans	Robots of Death
Chumblies	Polyphase Avatron
Yeti	Giant Robot
Quarks	Servo-Robot

3 Introducing Peter Davison – page 13

The correct order is as follows:

4 Which Planet? – page 14

1   S
2   A
3   H
4   D
5   A

If you re-arrange the letters S, A, H, D, A you can get the word SHADA which is the secret prison planet of the Time Lords.

5 The Nestenes – page 16

Numbers	1	2	3	4	5	6	7	8	9	10	11	12	13
Letters	A	I	Q	Y	B	J	R	Z	C	K	S	D	L

Numbers	14	15	16	17	18	19	20	21	22	23	24	25	26
Letters	T	E	M	U	F	N	V	G	O	W	H	P	X

Once the puzzle has been completed the grid will look like this:

6 The Yeti – page 18

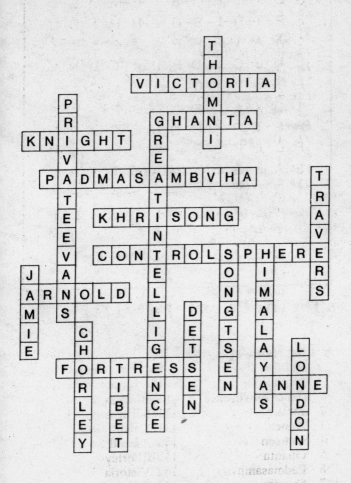

7 Milestones in the Doctor Who Saga – page 20

1   *The War Games*
2   *The Stones of Blood*
3   *The Dalek Invasion of Earth*
4   *The Dalek Masterplan*
5   *Fury from the Deep*
6   *Colony in Space*
7   *Revenge of the Cybermen*
8   *The Armageddon Factor*
9   *Enlightenment*
10 His début was in the 116th story.
11 *The Tenth Planet*
12 *The War Games*
13 *The Planet of the Spiders*
14 *Logopolis*
15 *The Caves of Androzani*

8 The Five Doctors – page 21

1   Time Lords
2   Gallifrey
3   Death Zone
4   The Dark Tower
5   Borusa
6   Master
7   Romana
8   Susan
9   Sarah Jane
10 Dalek
11 Flavia
12 Rassilon
13 Tomb
14 Immortality
15 Timescoop
16 Black Scrolls
17 Tegan
18 Turlough
19 Brigadier
20 Liz Shaw
21 Yates
22 Jamie
23 Zoe
24 Coronet
25 Ring
26 Yeti

```
B A N A M O R T G D Y A T E S
O N T H E T O F E R T L S I T
Y E R F I L L A G I L A S N
R M S Q P A D I Z Z L R R A
E K R V O T T S O A A E U
W H I E E O H R J T S B S
O B A R Y T A C A H R U S
T Y R E U W S M S I O R A Q
K C S B K I A N E M O N L K
R N K D C E G G M O B E I S
A D E A T H Z O N E I I S L
D L L G J H G U O L R U T S I
E B A I E T E G A N A N D A E
H S D R O L E M I T O U T R B
T O M B Z R C O R O N E T T O
```

9 Name That Date – page 23

1 Ten Sixty-Six (*The Time Meddler*)
2 Nineteen hundred and Eleven (*The Pyramids of Mars*)
3 Nineteen Sixty-Four (*Planet of the Giants*)
4 Two Thousand One Hundred and Sixty-Four (*The Dalek Invasion of Earth*)
5 Sixteen Sixty-Six (*The Visitation*)

6 Nineteen Hundred and Nine (*The Horror of Fang Rock*)
7 Eighteen Eighty-Nine (*The Talons of Weng-Chiang*)
8 Nineteen Thirty-Five (*The Abominable Snowmen*)
9 Seventeen Forty-Six (*The Highlanders*)
10 Nineteen Sixty-Six (*The Faceless Ones*)

10 From One to Five – page 24

1 Vraxoin	9	Exxilon
2 Jovanka	10	Tigella
3 Strella	11	Jethryk
4 Monitor	12	Foamasi
5 Peladon	13	Crinoth
6 Grugger	14	Cessair
7 Slyther	15	Faraday
8 Robomen	16	Forgill

C$_1$	A$_2$	S$_3$	T$_4$	R$_5$	O$_6$	V$_7$	A$_8$	L$_9$	V$_{10}$	A$_{11}$
I$_{12}$	N$_{13}$	F$_{14}$	E$_{15}$	R$_{16}$	N$_{17}$	O$_{18}$		T$_{19}$	H$_{20}$	E$_{21}$
D$_{22}$	O$_{23}$	M$_{24}$	I$_{25}$	N$_{26}$	A$_{27}$	T$_{28}$	O$_{29}$	R$_{30}$	S$_{31}$	
L$_{32}$	O$_{33}$	G$_{34}$	O$_{35}$	P$_{36}$	O$_{37}$	L$_{38}$	I$_{39}$	S$_{40}$		
T$_{41}$	H$_{42}$	E$_{43}$		R$_{44}$	E$_{45}$	S$_{46}$	C$_{47}$	U$_{48}$	E$_{49}$	
F$_{50}$	R$_{51}$	O$_{52}$	N$_{53}$	T$_{54}$	I$_{55}$	O$_{56}$	S$_{57}$			

11 Travelling in Space – page 26

Once the puzzle has been finished it looks like this:

```
S  B  S—T—A—R—L—I—N—E—R  M  N
M  J  E—P—O—R—T—O—N—Y—D  O  E
F  S—U—N—I—M—R—E—T  Z  F  N  V
S  G  T  X  E  Q  V  A  A  K  E  A  E
N—E—V—E—S—E—B—O—R—P  N  R  S
H  H  U  V  S  A  Z  L  D  R  O  C  Y
W  E—M—P—R—E—S—S  I  O  E  H  R
X  C  X  D  A  R  U  Z  S  B  S  S  E
F  A  U  V  Y  E  T  Y  I  E  A  S  V
E  T  R  R  T—A—R—D—I—S  B  H  O
P  E  X  D  T  M  Y  W  N  I  Y  I  C
N  P  O  O  Y  Q  P  G  X  X  K  P  E
B  S  C  C  F  H  I  Z  H  J  S  O  R
```

Numbers	1	2	3	4	5	6	7	8	9	10	11	12	13
Letters	A	H	O	V	B	I	P	W	C	J	Q	X	D

Numbers	14	15	16	17	18	19	20	21	22	23	24	25	26
Letters	K	R	Y	E	L	S	Z	F	M	T	G	N	U

12 T L A S E N P – page 28

1	Deva Loka	6	Argolis
2	Spiridon	7	Tigella
3	Zeta Minor	8	Zolfa-Thura
4	Chloris	9	Alzarius
5	Skonnos	10	Inter Minor

13 Fourth's Success – page 28

```
P L W-O-D-A-H - S F S I  G R T K
D C N V B-R-O-T-O-N Q H L M X
Y A Q R E T S A M P Y W L O F
U T R A L J H O G C X S E R N
M S O C-E-S-S-A-I-R A C D B B
S A T P E T R A W B N A I T
O R C G R D M H A N X R E U T
R D E T G Y E R F G I O R S N
V A L G F U G K E T A T G A O
A Y L I O A L G R C C H T H R
D D O G K S O Y W E G D N K I
Z A C S U U S T O-R-T-S U E G
E L E E E T F E-L-C-A-R-O T Y
R G H G H D-A-R-D-L-E N C U T
D S T-A-R-E-N-C-A-P-E-L D S S
```

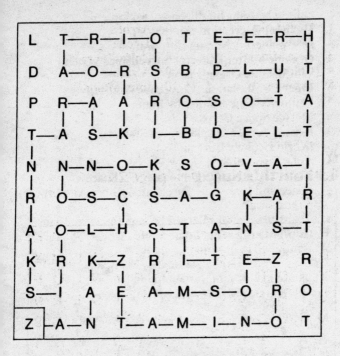

Zanak
Zeta Minor
Zeos
Mars
Titan
Kastria
Voga
Skonnos

Chloris
Karn
Tara
Skaro
Atrios
Ribos
Delta Three
Pluto

15 Doctor Who Abbreviations – page 31

1   United Nations Intelligence Taskforce
2   Tachyon Recreation Generator
3   Interplanetary Mining Corporation
4   Organic Matter Detector Surveillance System
5   World Zone Organization
6   Inner Constellations Corrective Authority
7   Pento-Cyleinic-Methyl-hydrane
8   Marine Space Corps
9   Hostile Action Displacement System
10 World Ecology Bureau
11 Total Survival Suit
12 Time And Relative Dimensions In Space
13 Space and Inter-time Directional Robot All-purpose
    Transporter
14 Transmission Of Matter Through Interstitial Time
15 Continuous Events Transmuter
16 Amplified Panatropic Compiler
17 Biomorphic Organizational Systems Supervisor
18 Charged Vacuum Emboitement
19 Will Operating Thought ANalogue
20 Scientific Reform Society

16 The Adventures – page 32

1   *Terminus*
2   *The Crusade*
3   *Shada*
4   *The Daemons*
5   *The Invasion*
6   *Full Circle*
7   *Kinda*
8   *Marco Polo*
9   *Inferno*
10 *Robot*
11 *Earthshock*
12 *The Chase*
13 *The Krotons*
14 *Castrovalva*
15 *The Rescue*
16 *Underworld*
17 *The Romans*
18 *Visitation*
19 *Meglos*
20 *Galaxy Four*
21 *Snakedance*
22 *The Savages*

23 *Logopolis*
24 *The Aztecs*
25 *Time-Flight*
26 *The Ark*
27 *The Daleks*

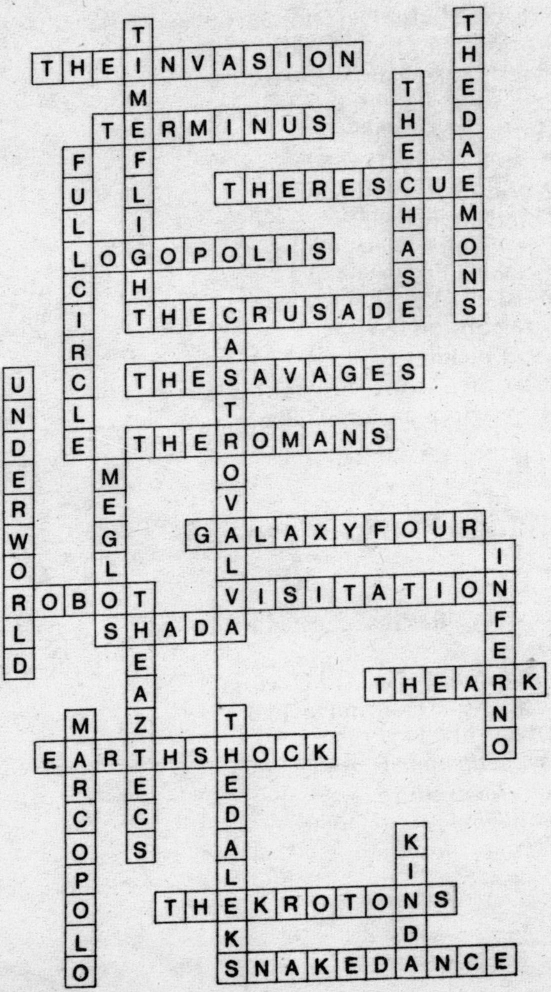

17 From First to Fifth – page 34

The correct order is as follows:

1 Carole Ann Ford (Susan)
2 Maureen O'Brien (Vicki)
3 Jackie Lane (Dodo)
4 Anneke Wills (Polly)
5 Frazer Hines (Jamie)
6 Wendy Padbury (Zoe)
7 Katy Manning (Jo)
8 Elisabeth Sladen (Sarah Jane)
9 Louise Jameson (Leela)
10 Mary Tamm (Romana)
11 Matthew Waterhouse (Adric)
12 Sarah Sutton (Nyssa)
13 Janet Fielding (Tegan)
14 Mark Strickson (Turlough)
15 Nicola Bryant (Perpugilliam)

18 Hidden Stories – page 34

The six story titles that can be found are:

The Mind Robber (second Doctor)
The Face of Evil (fourth Doctor)
The Aztecs (first Doctor)
The Twin Dilemma (sixth Doctor)
The Sea Devils (third Doctor)
The Awakening (fifth Doctor)

```
T T H E D A L E K S H E M R I
N S D T R O B B U E R T U H E
F O A N C E O N F S E O V I S
T I M E F L I G H T F L T H I
H T E M A M Z A T Y O E K C L
E N S N R T D H X N T C E T O
K O W E I A S A R H O N D I P
R T T L O L E E H B E M M O
O F A H L A F A S T O H E S G
T E A G G N R H D E R V I L O
O S E I K T H E C H A S E L
N M E L C R I C L L U F T H E
S A S N A K E D A N C E W A K
E T H E F I V E D O C T O R S
N I S N O M E D S G N I K N G
```

19 TOOCRD HOW VLENSO
– page 36

1 *State of Decay*
2 *Four to Doomsday*
3 *Planet of Evil*
4 *Horns of Nimon*
5 *Pyramids of Mars*
6 *Hand of Fear*
7 *Invisible Enemy*
8 *Android Invasion*
9 *Robots of Death*
10 *Face of Evil*

20 Bringing in UNIT – page 37

The correct order is as follows:

1   *The Invasion*
2   *Spearhead from Space*
3   *The Silurians*
4   *The Ambassadors of Death*
5   *Inferno*
6   *The Terror of the Autons*
7   *The Mind of Evil*
8   *Claws of Axos*
9   *The Daemons*
10 *The Day of the Daleks*
11 *The Time Monster*
12 *The Three Doctors*
13 *The Green Death*
14 *The Time Warrior*
15 *Invasion of the Dinosaurs*
16 *Planet of the Spiders*
17 *Robot*
18 *Terror of the Zygons*
19 *The Android Invasion*

21 Fifth's Enemies – page 38

Plasmatons   Mawdryn
Cybermen   Urbankans
Mara   Terileptils
Black Guardian   Omega
Eternals   Silurians
Master

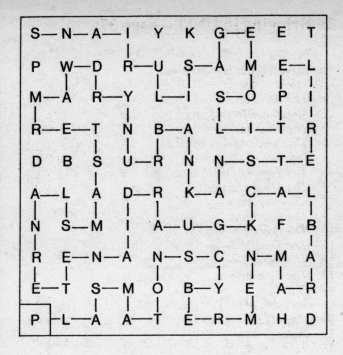

22 Odd-One-Out – page 39

1 Movellans. All the others are organic creatures but
   Movellans are sophisticated robots.
2 Japan. All the other countries have been visited by the
   Doctor.
3 Ribos. All the others have been visited by the Daleks.
4 Voga. All the others are connected in some way with
   the Key to Time.
5 Adric. He is the only one of the eight companions in
   the list who was killed.

6 *Meglos*. In all the other stories the Doctor had to
   defeat another Time Lord.
7 *The Ambassadors of Death*. All the others have been
   turned into Target novels.
8 Visians. All the others have tried to invade Earth.
9 *The Krotons*. All the other stories were written by
   Terry Nation.
10 Kraals. All the others were met by the second Doctor.

23 Find That Planet – page 40

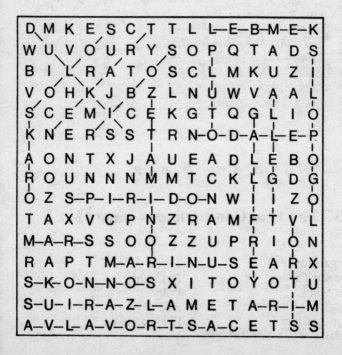

24 Set Down – page 41

25 The Loyal Companions – page 42

Tegan Jovanka
Steven Taylor
Liz Shaw
Nyssa
Ben Jackson
Adric

Leela
Jo Grant
Polly
Zoe
Dodo Chaplet
Vicki

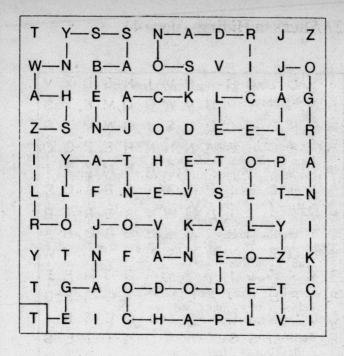

26 Name That Planet – page 43

1 A
2 O
3 S
4 R
5 K

If you re-arrange the letters A, O, S, R, K you get the name of the planet SKARO.

```
A  S  O  B  D  R  A  H  V  I  N  S  D  X  V
R  N  N  F  I  P  U  V  W  G  Q  M  K  Y  S
N  O  S  O  Z  C  O  L  S  J  O  N  M  T  R
H  R  E  C  E  O  A  N  K  N  R  E  P  Q  O
M  E  G  U  R  L  A  D  O  N  H  M  Z  Z  I
O  X  J  D  L  I  E  I  X  T  S  R  A  O  R
R  M  S  A  C  I  D  M  W  N  S  E  R  I  R
O  Y  B  L  M  S  T  V  A  E  F  B  B  B  A
K  N  U  E  A  Y  M  E  S  H  D  Y  I  V  W
S  D  X  K  C  I  T  R  Y  G  C  C  H  E  E
P  W  F  S  R  N  A  S  N  O  T  O  R  K  C
O  U  S  N  A  E  N  O  D  I  D  L  C  K  I
R  I  L  L  S  S  E  N  S  O  R  I  T  E  S
J  T  T  Z  F  R  E  F  U  S  I  A  N  S  H
N  A  R  E  T  P  O  N  E  M  U  Y  I  J  O
```

28 The Ice Warriors – page 45

1 Ice Warriors
2 Mars
3 Varga
4 Ioniser
5 Peladon
6 Trisilicate
7 Izlyr
8 Ssorg
9 Galactic Federation
10 Martian Seed Pods

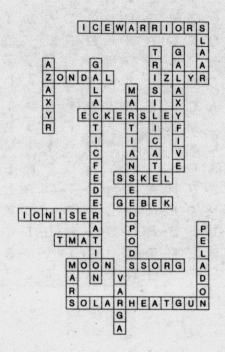

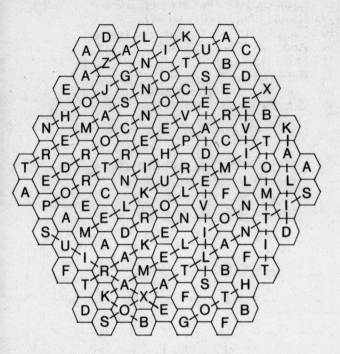

30 The Novels – page 48

1. Barry Letts – *The Daemons*
2. David Whitaker – *The Daleks*
3. Gerry Davis – *The Cybermen*
4. Christopher H. Bidmead – *Logopolis*
5. Ian Marter – *The Sontaran Experiment*

6 Terrance Dicks – *The State of Decay*
7 John Lydecker – *Warriors' Gate*
8 Brian Hayles – *The Curse of Peladon*
9 David Fisher – *The Leisure Hive*
10 Malcolm Hulke – *The Dinosaur Invasion*
11 Andrew Smith – *Full Circle*
12 Philip Hinchcliffe – *The Keys of Marinus*
13 Bill Strutton – *The Zarbi*
14 Eric Saward – *The Visitation*
15 Peter Grimwade – *Time-Flight*

31 Exterminate! Exterminate! – page 49

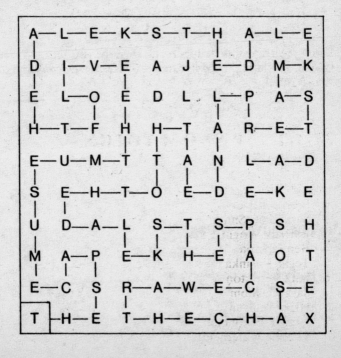

The Space Museum
The Evil of the Daleks
The Dalek Masterplan
Death to the Daleks
The Space War
The Chase
The Daleks

32 Name That Enemy – page 50

1 A
2 O
3 G
4 E
5 M

If you re-arrange the letters A, O, G, E, M you get
OMEGA whom the Doctor met in *The Three Doctors* and
Arc of Infinity.

33 HET PNSOMAOICN –
page 52

1   Steven Taylor
2   Sarah Jane Smith
3   Barbara Wright
4   Ben Jackson
5   Tegan Jovanka
6   Ian Chesterton
7   Sara Kingdom
8   Harry Sullivan
9   Jamie McCrimmon
10 Victoria Waterfield

34 Do You Know Your Doctor Who Facts? – page 53

1	Duggan	9	Salamar	17	Replica
2	Andor	10	Argolis	18	Camilla
3	Oracle	11	Issigri	19	Lazlo
4	Leeson	12	Ribos	20	Login
5	Neman	13	Oseidon	21	Inferno
6	Aneth	14	Noah	22	Omega
7	Thawn	15	Habris	23	Galleia
8	Nyssa	16	Styre	24	Adric

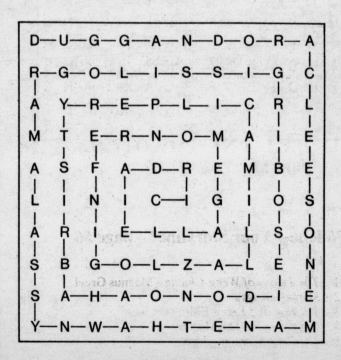

```
O N T L H A D N E F H E F I C
C A S T E L L A N R S T M P A
O N H D A Y T N E D I S E R P
O F O T H E M O N T S E S Y I
H N B O V A R D A N S N N D T
F V O R T E X S A X A O A O O
P R G C I L I R X E M Z Y N L
T H A Q I D A I C R E H N I B
O U N R R T R G A T O T I A F
M E S A N T P H U A N A M N G
I N T O A W F O H R I E C S H
T H S M E O A U N P A D A H S
T H O R E O A R C A L I A N C
T H E Y R O M A N C P E O F T
G R E A T V A M P I R E H E R
```

36 Know Your Storyline? – page 56

1 *The Talons of Weng-Chiang* – Magnus Greel
2 *Shada* – Skagra
3 *The Hand of Fear* – Eldrad
4 *Castrovalva* – The Master
5 *The Time Warrior* – Linx

37 The Cybermen – page 57

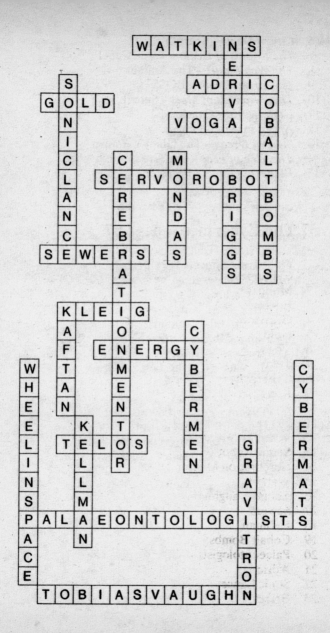

38 The Stars – page 59

1 Frazer Hines – Jamie McCrimmon
2 Deborah Watling – Victoria Waterfield
3 Ian Marter – Harry Sullivan
4 Maureen O'Brien – Vicki
5 Carole Ann Ford – Susan
6 Janet Fielding – Tegan Jovanka
7 William Russell – Ian Chesterton
8 Katy Manning – Jo Grant
9 Nicholas Courtney – The Brigadier
10 Sarah Sutton – Nyssa
11 Jacqueline Hill – Barbara Wright
12 Michael Craze – Ben Jackson
13 Peter Purves – Steven Taylor
14 John Levene – Benton
15 Matthew Waterhouse – Adric
16 Jean Marsh – Sara Kingdom
17 Richard Franklin – Captain Yates
18 Mary Tamm – Romana (first incarnation)
19 Mark Strickson – Turlough
20 Elisabeth Sladen – Sarah Jane Smith
21 Jackie Lane – Dodo Chaplet
22 Louise Jameson – Leela
23 Nicola Bryant – Perpugilliam Brown
24 Wendy Padbury – Zoe Herriot
25 Lalla Ward – Romana (second incarnation)
26 Adrienne Hill – Katarina
27 Anneke Wills – Polly
28 Caroline John – Liz Shaw

39 The Sontarans – page 60

Once the puzzle has been completed the grid will look like this.

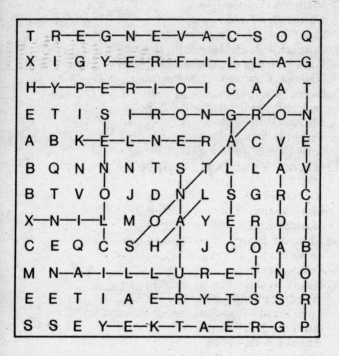

Numbers	1	2	3	4	5	6	7	8	9	10	11	12	13
Letters	A	E	J	N	S	W	B	F	K	O	T	X	C

Numbers	14	15	16	17	18	19	20	21	22	23	24	25	26
Letters	G	L	P	U	Y	D	H	M	Q	V	Z	I	R

40 Mystery Companion – page 62

1 A
2 E
3 G
4 N
5 T

If you re-arrange the letters, A, E, G, N, T you get
TEGAN who was one of the fifth Doctor's companions.
She made her last appearance in *Resurrection of the
Daleks*, although she was seen briefly in *The Caves of
Androzani*.

41 Ugh! What Is It? – page 64

Krotons
Terileptils
Daleks
Cybermen
Movellans
Drashigs

Zygons
Krargs
Sensorites
Sontarans
Nimon
Tythonians

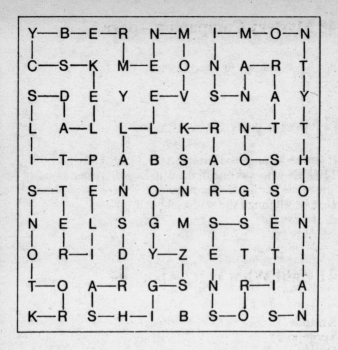

42 The Doctor vs. The Master – page 65

1 Tom Baker (the fourth Doctor)
2 Peter Pratt (the Master in *The Deadly Assassin*)
3 Patrick Troughton (the second Doctor)
4 Anthony Ainley (the Master in his second screen incarnation)
5 Colin Baker (the sixth Doctor)
6 Roger Delgado (the Master in his first screen incarnation)
7 Peter Davison (the fifth Doctor)

8   William Hartnell (the first Doctor)
9   Geoffrey Beevers (the Master in *The Keeper of Traken*)
10   Jon Pertwee (the third Doctor)

43 Mystery Story – page 66

The stories are as follows:

1   *Earthshock*
2   *Time-Flight*
3   *The Invasion*
4   *Meglos*
5   *Enlightenment*
6   *The Daemons*
7   *Warriors from the Deep*
8   *The Leisure Hive*
9   *The Armageddon Factor*
10   *Terminus*
11   *The Ice Warriors*
12   *Mawdryn Undead*
13   *The Nightmare of Eden*
14   *The Horns of Nimon*

The fourteen letters are: E, T, I, M, E, D, W, L, A, T, I, M, N, H. When these letters are re-arranged they give *The Twin Dilemma*.

44 Planet Search – page 67

```
S-I-R-I-S-O-R-E-T-S-E-A-H-P  E
N  Q  S  K  F  A  C  R  H  K  L  Y  T  I  D
G  U  A-N-G-A-M-A-T-L-E-D  T  O  V
J  R  L  Z  A-R-A-T-N-O-S  X  E  P  W
O  M  Z  B  S  Q  E  P  F  T  D  W  N  S  A
A  I  A  Y  N  L  E  E  B  E  X  S  A  A  Z
R  V  R  S  R  D  U  L  V  O  J  U  L  H  O
I  C  I  U  E  K  G  A  P  H  M  I  P  P  S
M  D  U  N  F  L  L  D  H  K  R  D  H  I  E
D  S  S  I  M  O  V  O  A  P  I  I  T  R  I
B  Z  R  R  K  N  J  N  C  I  B  R  F  E  D
R-U-T-A-T-H-R-E-E  T  O  A  I  X  O  N
Y  J  X  M  M  S  W  O  Q  V  S  G  F  E  N
R  F  S-E-N-S-E-S-P-H-E-R-E  B  N
R  M-E-T-E-B-E-L-I-S-T-H-R-E-E
```

1	Peladon	11	Phaester Osiris
2	Skaro	12	Ruta Three
3	Fifth Planet	13	Sense-Sphere
4	Metebelis Three	14	Ribos
5	Mars	15	Sontara
6	Deva Loka	16	Delta Magna
7	Oseidon	17	Mira
8	Eden	18	Marinus
9	Alzarius	19	Xeriphas
10	Aridius	20	Vortis

45 Planet Choice – page 68

1   E
2   M
3   B
4   E
5   L
6   K

If you re-arrange the letters E, M, B, E, L, K you can get KEMBEL which was visited by the first Doctor in *The Dalek Masterplan*. This planet was ravaged by the Time Destructor.

46 The Daleks – page 70

1	Daleks	13	Ogrons
2	Time Destructor	14	Space War
3	Taranium	15	Master
4	Davros	16	Movellans
5	Thals	17	Spiridon
6	Kaleds	18	Icecano
7	Chen	19	Vaber
8	Kembel	20	Vulcan
9	Skaro	21	Travel Machines
10	Exxilon	22	Aridius
11	Parrinium	23	Monk
12	Cory		

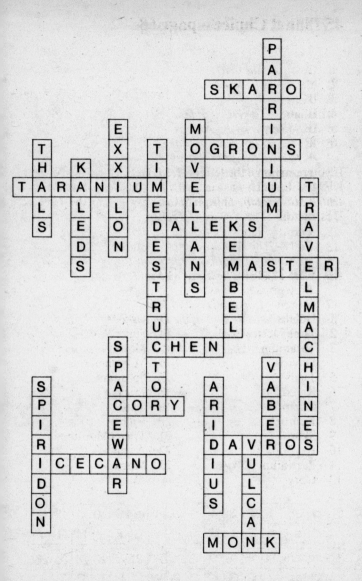

47 The Companions – page 72

1   Adric – *Full Circle*
2   Dodo – *The Massacre*
3   Harry – *Robot*
4   Jamie – *The Highlanders*
5   Jo – *Terror of the Autons*
6   Katarina – *The Myth Makers*
7   K9 – *The Invisible Enemy*
8   Kamelion – *The King's Demons*
9   Leela – *The Face of Evil*
10   Liz – *Spearhead from Space*
11   Nyssa – *The Keeper of Traken*
12   Perpugilliam – *Planet of Fire*
13   Polly – *The War Machines*
14   Romana – *The Ribos Operation*
15   Sarah Jane – *The Time Warrior*
16   Steven – *The Chase*
17   Tegan – *Logopolis*
18   Victoria – *The Evil of the Daleks*
19   Vicki – *The Rescue*
20   Zoe – *The Wheel in Space*

48 UNIT – page 73

Numbers	1	2	3	4	5	6	7	8	9	10	11	12	13
Letters	A	E	I	M	Q	U	Y	B	F	J	N	R	V

Numbers	14	15	16	17	18	19	20	21	22	23	24	25	26
Letters	Z	C	G	K	O	S	W	D	H	L	P	T	X

Once the puzzle has been completed the grid will look like this:

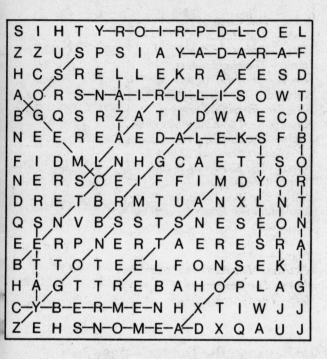

49 Track-A-Story – page 75

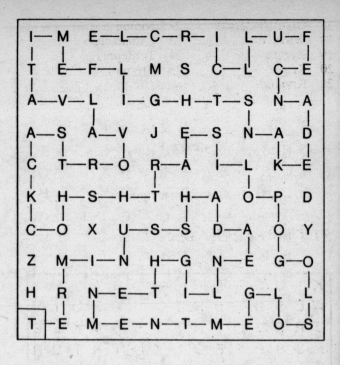

50 Aliens vs. the Doctor – page 76

The correct order is as follows:

1	Daleks	9	Ice Warriors
2	Voords	10	Dominators
3	Zarbi	11	Krotons
4	Drahvins	12	Silurians
5	Cybermen	13	Primords
6	Macra	14	Daemons
7	Chameleons	15	Sea Devils
8	Yeti	16	Sontarans

51 Time Search – page 77

```
K T U C A D R-E-M-O-G A T H I
W L S-U-I-B-R-O-M F R B U I V
J R F G-O-T-H E Y S B M K L E
P J S P F E G U K O I R T D R
X L N Z M A Q O R M P A C R E
P A R L V A S U T R N S H E N
K Y E O P U S F O B R S L D L
F P N F X A T T C Y X I L K E
I E G C A V C F E Z R L E U K
N I I C R O R D A R K O R K X
I S N H D D J T B G N N D K O
D H C O C L X N-A-D-O-R N M V
E C O B S R R L V T M X A P H
H J G N-I-V-A-Y-L-A-S M P K A
A-N-D-R-E-D F W I Z W U S D Y
```

125

52 Number 5 vs. Omega – page 78

Once all the letters have been filled in, the grid looks like this:

```
W  R  Y  Z  F  N—I—B—O—R  Q  G  L  J  M
D  V  Q  D—A—M—O—N  B  G  B  X  N  Y  A
B—O—R—U—S—A  I  W  A  A  I  R  Q  T  T
C  L  B  G  Z  T  M  L  V  S  O  E  Y  I  T
O  U  T  J  N  R  L  P  M  G  D  T  R  N  E
F  L  N  E  I  K  U  A  C  C  A  S  O  I  R
K  M  I  J  F  X  D  F  G  B  T  O  L  F  C
R  Q  D  R  E  R  A  N  D  U  A  O  A  N  O
W  X  E  V  E  C—A—R—O—Z  B  B  T  I  N
B  Y  H  T—H—A—L—I—A  B  N  N  U  F  V
Q  D  S  E  G  H  U  D  I  E  N  O  A  O  E
B  M  A  G  B  T  K  J  D  I  G  I  G  C  R
A  W  H  A  M—A—X—I—L  L  N  S  J  R  T
Y  E  D  N  P  T  O  O  C  A  M  U  N  A  E
O  Z  V  S  S  P  C—R—Y—P—T  F  F  C  R
```

Numbers	1	2	3	4	5	6	7	8	9	10	11	12	13
Letters	A	G	L	Q	V	B	H	M	R	W	C	I	N

Numbers	14	15	16	17	18	19	20	21	22	23	24	25	26
Letters	S	X	D	J	O	T	Y	E	K	P	U	Z	F

126

53 Featuring the Dalek! page 80

The correct order is as follows:
1   *The Daleks*
2   *The Dalek Invasion of Earth*
3   *The Space Museum*
4   *The Chase*
5   *Mission to the Unknown*
6   *The Dalek Masterplan*
7   *The Power of the Daleks*
8   *The Evil of the Daleks*
9   *Day of the Daleks*
10 *Frontier in Space*
11 *Planet of the Daleks*
12 *Death to the Daleks*
13 *Genesis of the Daleks*
14 *Destiny of the Daleks*
15 *The Five Doctors*
16 *The Resurrection of the Daleks*

54 Alien Attack – page 81

Daleks   Sontarans
Cybermen   Rutans
Kraals   Zygons
Ice Warriors   Mandragora
Chameleons   Krynoids
Nestenes   Wirrn
Axos

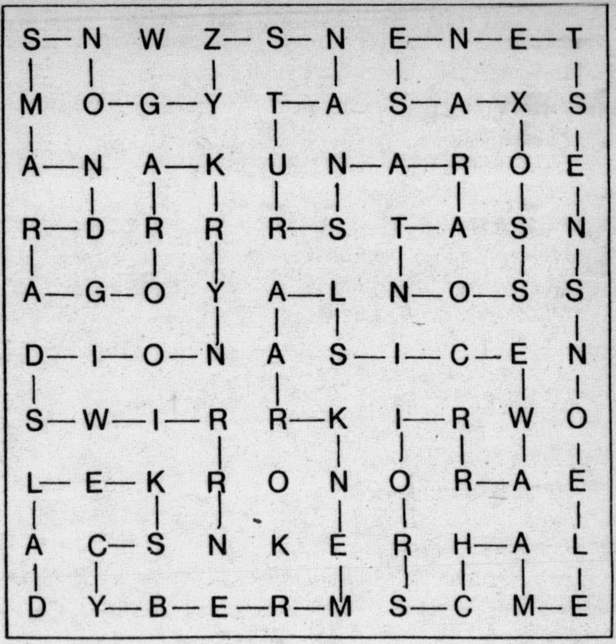
S N W Z S N E N E T
M O G Y T A S A X S
A N A K U N A R O E
R D R R R S T A S N
A G O Y A L N O S S
D I O N A S I C E N
S W I R R K I R W O
L E K R O N O R A E
A C S N K E R H A L
D Y B E R M S C M E